# SWEENEY TODD

## THE DEMON BARBER OF FLEET STREET

### WORDS AND MUSIC BY STEPHEN SONDHEIM

ALFRED

Alfred Publishing Co., Inc.
16320 Roscoe Blvd., Suite 100
P.O. Box 10003
Van Nuys, CA 91410-0003
alfred.com

DreamWorks Pictures®

ISBN-10: 1-7390-5154-7
ISBN-13: 978-1-7390-5154-2

STEPHEN SONDHEIM wrote the music and lyrics for A FUNNY THING HAPPENED ON THE WAY TO THE FORUM (1962), ANYONE CAN WHISTLE (1964), COMPANY (1970), FOLLIES (1971), A LITTLE NIGHT MUSIC (1973), THE FROGS (1974), PACIFIC OVERTURES (1976), SWEENEY TODD (1979), MERRILY WE ROLL ALONG (1981), SUNDAY IN THE PARK WITH GEORGE (1984), INTO THE WOODS (1987), ASSASSINS (1991), PASSION (1994) and BOUNCE (2003), as well as lyrics for WEST SIDE STORY (1957), GYPSY (1959), DO I HEAR A WALTZ? (1965) and additional lyrics for CANDIDE (1973). SIDE BY SIDE BY SONDHEIM (1976), MARRY ME A LITTLE (1981), YOU'RE GONNA LOVE TOMORROW (1983), PUTTING IT TOGETHER (1993/99) and MOVING ON (2001) are anthologies of his work as composer and lyricist. For films, he composed the scores of "Stavisky" (1974) and co-composed "Reds" (1981) as well as songs for "Dick Tracy" (1990). He also wrote the songs for the television production "Evening Primrose" (1966), co-authored the film "The Last of Sheila" (1973) and the play GETTING AWAY WITH MURDER (1996) and provided incidental music for the plays THE GIRLS OF SUMMER (1956), INVITATION TO A MARCH (1961), TWIGS (1971) and THE ENCLAVE (1973). SATURDAY NIGHT (1954), his first professional musical, finally had its New York premiere in 1999. Mr. Sondheim is on the Council of the Dramatists Guild, the National Association of Playwrights, Composers and Lyricists, having served as its President from 1973 to 1981, in which year he founded Young Playwrights Inc. to develop and promote the work of American playwrights ages 18 years and younger.

# CONTENTS

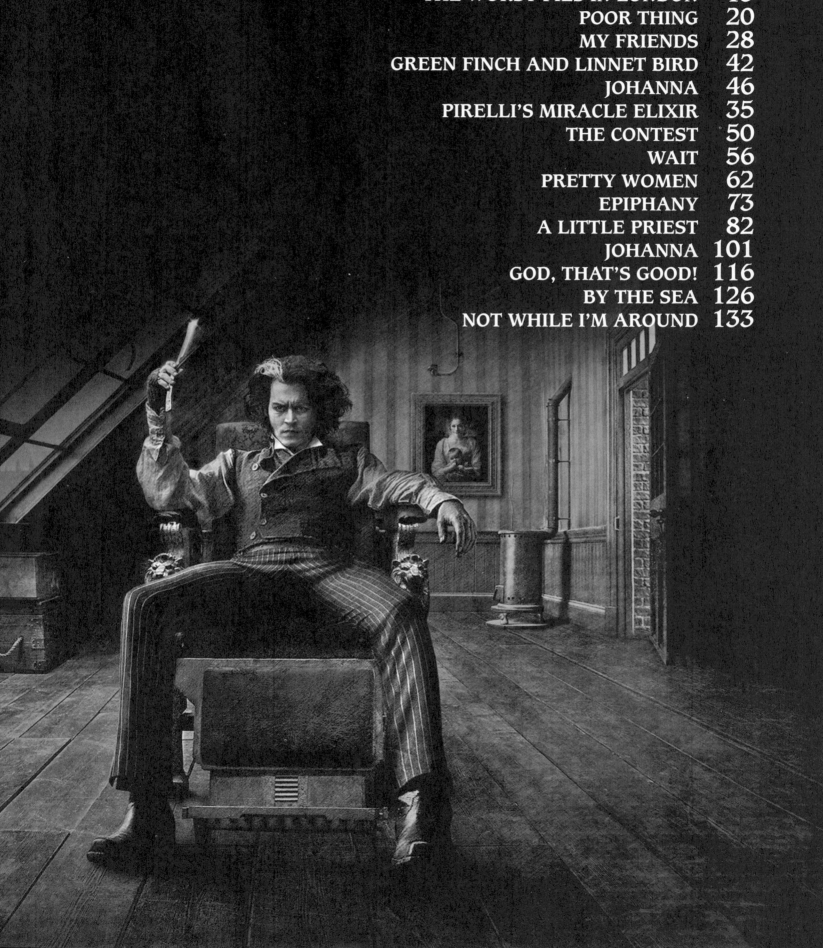

# NO PLACE LIKE LONDON

Music and Lyrics by
STEPHEN SONDHEIM

worth what a pig could spit, and it goes by the name of Lon - don.

At the top of the hole sit the priv - 'leged few, mak - ing

mock of the ver - min in the low - er zoo, turn - ing beau - ty in - to filth and greed. I, too, have

sailed the world and seen its won - ders, for the cru - el - ty of men is as

8

*My mind is far from easy.*

*In these once familiar streets, I feel shadows…*

*…everywhere.*

**TODD:** *a tempo*

There was a  bar-ber and his wife,  and she was  beau-ti-ful.__

A  fool-ish  bar-ber and his wife.  She was his  rea - son and  his  life,

and she was beau-ti-ful.___ And she was

vir-tu-ous, and he was na-ïve.___

There was an-

oth-er man who saw that she was beau-ti-ful.___ A pi-ous

*dolce*

*ten.*

*mp* *mf*

*subito* *p* *mf* *subito*

*a tempo*

*a tempo*
*mp*

12

# THE WORST PIES IN LONDON

Music and Lyrics by
STEPHEN SONDHEIM

**Allegretto agitato (♩ = 112)**

**MRS. LOVETT:**

Wait! What's yer rush? What's yer hur-ry? You gave me such a

fright, I thought you was a ghost! Half a min-ute, can't-cher? Sit! Sit ye down! *Sit!* All I meant is that I

have-n't seen a cus-tom-er for weeks. Did you come here for a pie, sir? Do for-give me if me

The Worst Pies in London - 7 - 1
30013

16

cede it. It's noth-ing but crust-ing. Here, drink this, you'll need it. The

worst pies in Lon - don. And no won-der, with the price of

*mf*

**Tempo I**

meat what it is when you get it. Nev-er thought I'd live to see the day men-'d think it was a

*f mf*  *f mf*  *f mf*  *f mf*

treat find-ing poor an-i-mals wot are dy-ing in the street. Mrs.__ Moo-ney has a

*f mf*  *f mf*  *f mf*

18

**Meno mosso, sempre rubato**

hard, sir. E - ven hard - er than the worst pies in Lon - don.

On - ly lard and noth - ing more. Is that just re - volt - ing? All

greas - y and grit - ty. It looks like it's

molt - ing and tastes like... Well, pit - y a

The Worst Pies in London - 7 - 6
30013

# POOR THING

Music and Lyrics by
STEPHEN SONDHEIM

**Todd:** *You have a room over the shop, don't you? Times are so hard, why don't you rent it out?*

**Mrs. Lovett:** *People think it's haunted.*

**Todd:** *Haunted?*    **Mrs. Lovett:** *Yeah, and who's to say they're wrong? You see, years ago something happened up there… something not very nice.*

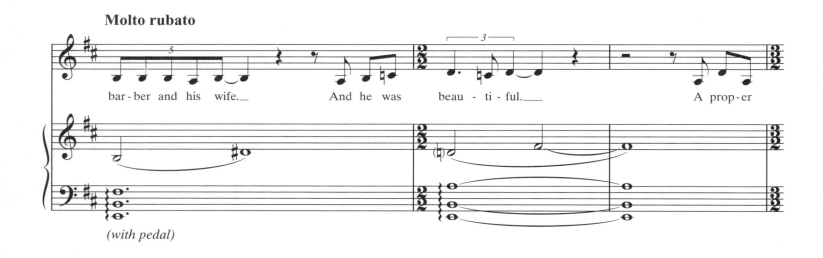

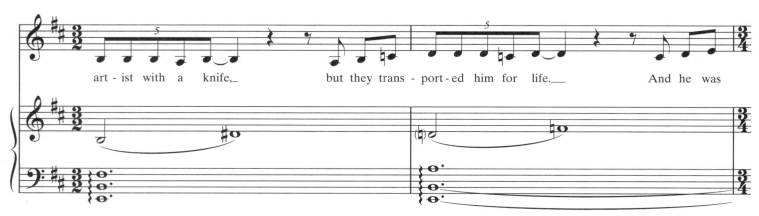

Poor Thing - 8 - 1
30013

**A tempo, delicato (in 3)**

beau - ti - ful.___

*Barker, his name was. Benjamin Barker.*

**Todd:** *What was his crime?*

**Mrs. Lovett:** *Foolishness.* He had this

wife, you see.___ Pret - ty lit - tle thing. Sil - ly lit - tle nit had her

chance for the moon on a string.___ Poor

22

thing. _____ Poor thing. _____

There was this judge, you see; _____

want-ed her like mad. Ev-'ry day he'd send her a flow-er.

But did she come down from her tow-er? Sat up there and

Poor Thing - 8 - 3
30013

**Moderato cantabile**

Bea - dle calls on her, all po - lite. Poor thing._____ Poor

thing._____ The judge, he tells her, is all con - trite. He

blames him - self for her dread - ful plight. She must come straight to his

house to - night. Poor thing. Poor thing.

where is Judge Tur - pin?" she asks.
He was there, all right! On - ly not so con - trite!
She was - n't no match for such craft, you see, and
ev - 'ry - one thought it so droll._____ They fig - ured she had to be

*f*

*mf cresc. poco a poco*

daft,  you  see.  So  all  of  them  stood  there  and

laughed,  you  see.  Poor  soul!  Poor  thing!

**Todd:** *No! Would no one have mercy on her?*

**Mrs. Lovett:** *So, it is you! Benjamin Barker.*

**Todd:** *No! No Barker. That man is dead. It's Todd, now, Sweeney Todd, and he will have his revenge.*

*ff furioso*

# MY FRIENDS

Music and Lyrics by
STEPHEN SONDHEIM

Home,_____ and we're to - geth - er,____

and we'll do won - ders,___ won't we?___

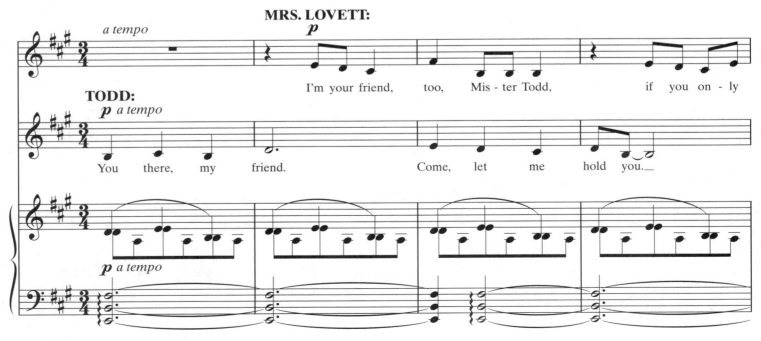

MRS. LOVETT:

I'm your friend, too, Mis - ter Todd, if you on - ly

TODD:

You there, my friend. Come, let me hold you.___

**A tempo, sempre dolce**

**Todd:** *At last! My arm is complete again!*

Meno mosso, ben marcato

# PIRELLI'S MIRACLE ELIXIR

Music and Lyrics by
STEPHEN SONDHEIM

cov - er your pil - low is cov - ered with hair Wot ought not to be

there? Well, La - dies and gen - tle - men, From now on you can

wak - en at ease._____ You need nev - er a - gain have a wor - ry or care, I will

show you a mir - a - cle mar - vel - ous rare._____

Gen-tle-men, you are a-bout to see some-thing that rose from the dead...

**L'istesso tempo**

...on the top of my head!

'Twas Pi-rel-li's Mir-a-cle E-lix-ir That's wot did the trick, sir,

True, sir, true. Was it quick, sir? Did it in a tick, sir,

37

Pirelli's Miracle Elixir - 7 - 3
30013

When they see how thick, sir, You can have your pick, sir, of the girls!

Want to buy a bot-tle, mis-sus?

(MRS. LOVETT:) *f*
What is this?

(TODD:) *f*
What is this? Smells like

Smells like... phew!

Would-n't touch it if I was you, dear.

piss.

Looks like piss.

This is piss. Piss with

# GREEN FINCH AND LINNET BIRD

Music and Lyrics by
STEPHEN SONDHEIM

**Adagio ma non troppo, poco rubato (♩ = 112)**

# JOHANNA
## (Anthony)

Music and Lyrics by
STEPHEN SONDHEIM

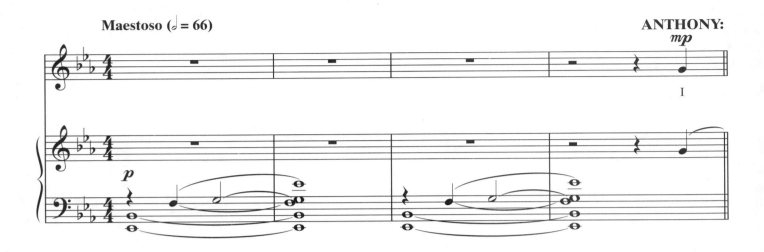

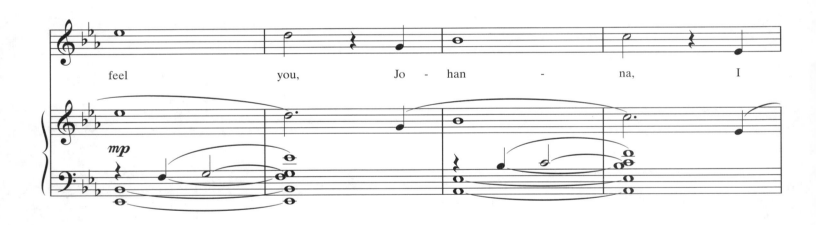

satisfied enough to dream____ you. Happily, I was mistaken, Johanna!_____ I'll

steal you, Johanna, I'll steal you.

Do they think that walls can hide____ you? Even now, I'm at your win-

Till I'm with you then, I'm with you there, sweet-ly bur-ied in your yel-low hair.

# THE CONTEST

Music and Lyrics by
STEPHEN SONDHEIM

The Contest - 6 - 1
30013

nerve-a to say____ my e-lix-ir is piss!          Who says this?!

**TODD:**
*I do. I am Mr. Sweeney Todd of Fleet Street.
I have opened a bottle of Pirelli's elixir, and I say to you
that it is nothing but an errant fraud, concoted from
piss and ink.  And furthermore – "Signor"– I have
serviced no kings, yet I wager I can shave a cheek with
ten times more dexterity than any street mountebank!*

**PIRELLI:**
*You hear zis foolish man? Now, please, you will see
how he will regret his folly!*

**TODD:**
*Who's for a free shave? Will Beadle Bamford be the judge?*

**BEADLE:**
*Glad, as always, to oblige my friends and neighbors.
The fastest, smoothest shave is the winner.*

**Agitato**  = 144

**L'istesso tempo (♩ = ♩.)**

Now, si - gno - ri - ni, si - gno - ri, we mix - a da lath - er, but first - a you

gath - er a - round. Si - gno - ri - ni, si - gno - ri, you look - ing a man who have

had - a da glo - ry to shave - a da Pope! Mis - ter Swee - ney who - ev - er- I

beg - a your par - don - 'll prob - a - bly say it was on - ly a car - di - nal.

# WAIT

Music and Lyrics by
STEPHEN SONDHEIM

**Adagio espressivo ma non rubato** (♩ = 112)

Wait - 6 - 1
30013

**MRS. LOVETT:**

Eas - y now.___ Hush, love, hush.___ Don't dis - tress___ your - self,

What's your rush?___ Keep your thoughts___ Nice and lush.___

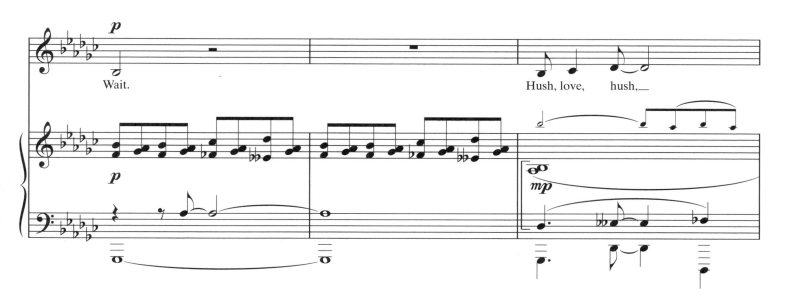

Wait. Hush, love, hush,___

Think it through._ Once it bub - bles, then what's to do?____

Watch it close._ Let it brew._ Wait.

I've been think - ing, flow - ers, May-be dai - sies,____ To

bright-en up the room..._____ Don't you think some flow - ers,____ pret-ty

those who can___ Wait.

Gil - ly - flow - ers may - be, 'stead of dai - sies... I don't know, though...

What do you think?

# PRETTY WOMEN

Music and Lyrics by
STEPHEN SONDHEIM

**Allegretto grazioso (♩ = 144)**

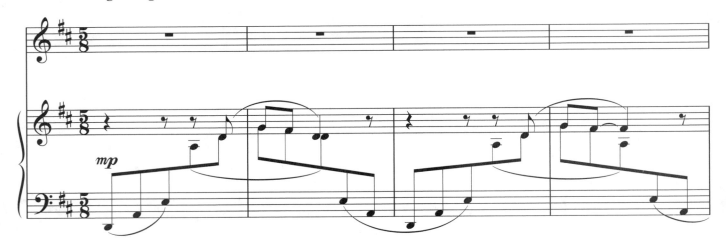

JUDGE: *mf*

You

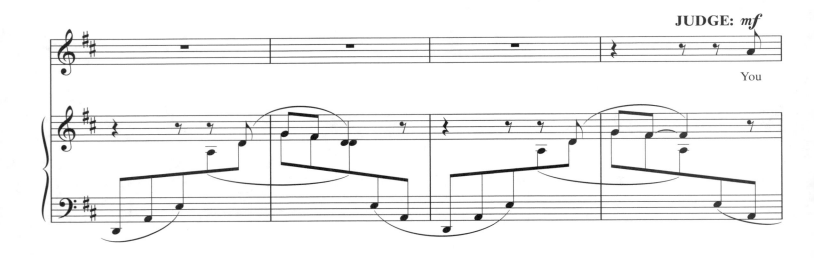

see, sir, a man in-fat-u-ate with love, Her ar-dent and ea-ger slave, So

64

(TODD:) *mf*

(Judge:) *You are in a merry mood today, Mr. Todd.* 'Tis your de-light, sir, catch-ing fi - re from

one man to the next.

(JUDGE:) *mf*

'Tis true, sir, love can still in-spi-re the

What more can man re-qui-re?

blood to pound, The heart leap high-er, What more can man re-qui-re than

More than love, sir. Wom-en. Pret-ty wom-en.
love, sir? What, sir? Ah, yes, wom-en.
dim.
(Jauntily) mf
8vb
(Hums) Bum - bum - bum - bum - bum - bum - ba - da - dum - bum - bum (etc.)
mp
(Whistles)
(8vb)

**Slowly** (♩ = 72)

**TODD:** *(To the razor)*

Now then, my friend,

Now to your pur-pose.___ Pa - tience, en - joy it, Re - venge can't be

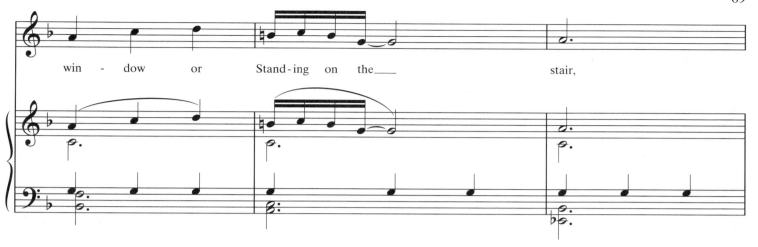

win - dow or Stand - ing on the___ stair,

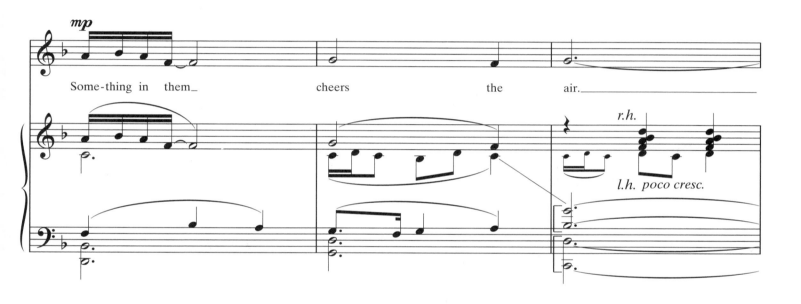

Some-thing in them___ cheers the air.___

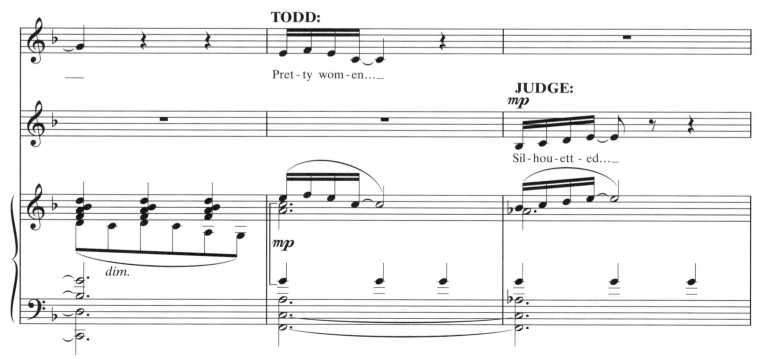

**TODD:**

Pret - ty wom - en...___

**JUDGE:**

Sil - hou - ett - ed...___

70

Pretty Women - 11 - 9
30013

72

# EPIPHANY

Music and Lyrics by
STEPHEN SONDHEIM

**Anthony:** *Mister Todd – you have to help me – Mister Todd, please. Mister Todd.*

**Todd:** *Out. Out!*

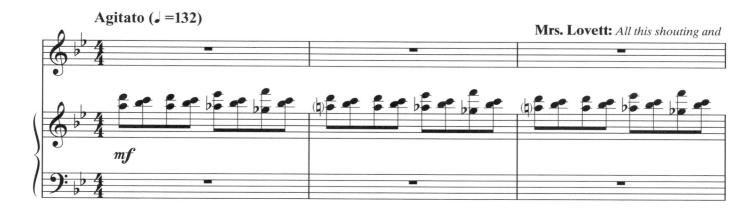

76

one man, no, Nor ten men, Nor a hun-dred can as-suage me— I will

**Moderato alla marcia** (♩ = 80)

have you!

*And I will get him back, e-ven as he gloats. In the*

*mean-time I'll prac-tice on less hon-or-a-ble throats. And my*

(Keening again)

Lu - cy lies in ash - es, And I'll nev - er see my girl a - gain, But the

work waits, I'm a - live at last, And I'm

full of joy!

# A LITTLE PRIEST

Music and Lyrics by
STEPHEN SONDHEIM

**Mrs. Lovett:** *That's all very well, but what are we going to do about him?*
**Todd:** *Later on, when it's dark, we'll take him to some secret place and bury him.*
**Mrs. Lovett:** *Oh yeah, of course, we could do that.*

**Rubato (♩ = 120)**

**Mrs. Lovett:** *I don't suppose he's got any relatives going to come poking around looking for him.*

Seems a down-right shame.

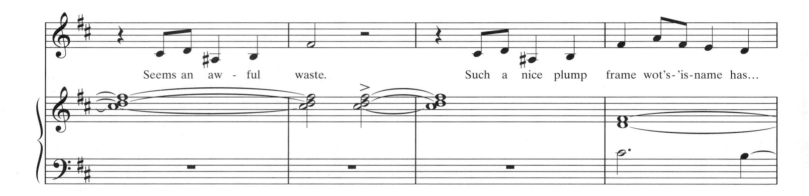

Seems an aw-ful waste. Such a nice plump frame wot's-'is-name has...

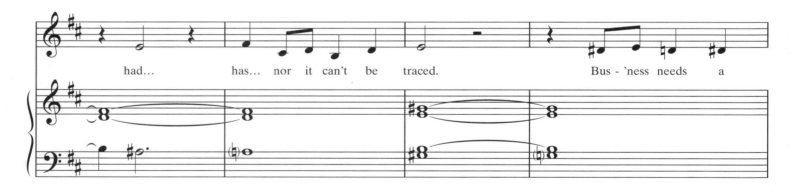

had... has... nor it can't be traced. Bus-'ness needs a

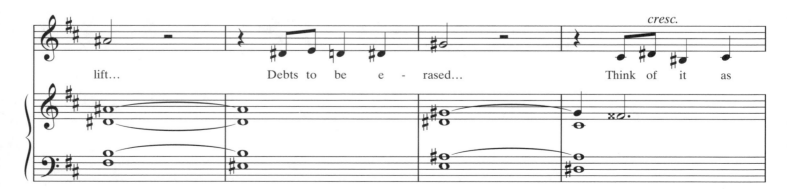

lift... Debts to be e-rased... Think of it as

84

A Little Priest - 19 - 3
30013

A Little Priest - 19 - 5
30013

Then who are we to de-ny it in man, my dear,

And who are we to de-ny it in here?

here?

**Todd:** *These are desperate times, Mrs. Lovett, and desperate*

*mp subito*

*measures are called for.*

**Mrs. Lovett:** *Here we are, hot out*

*of the oven.*

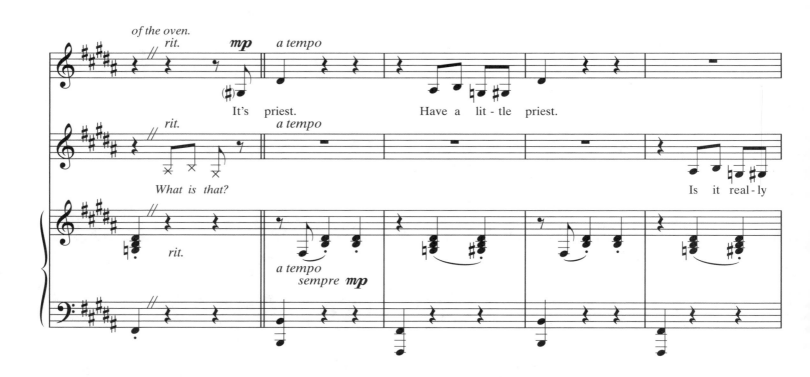

It's    priest.                    Have a   lit - tle    priest.

What  is   that?                                                                Is    it   real - ly

Sir,   it's    too  good,      at    least.                    Then  a - gain, they   don't   com - mit

good?

No, you see, the trou - ble with po - et is,

*that?*

how do you know it's de - ceased? Try the

priest.

*dim. poco a poco*

92

A Little Priest - 19 - 11
30013

96

# JOHANNA
### (Anthony, Todd, Beggar Woman)

Music and Lyrics by
STEPHEN SONDHEIM

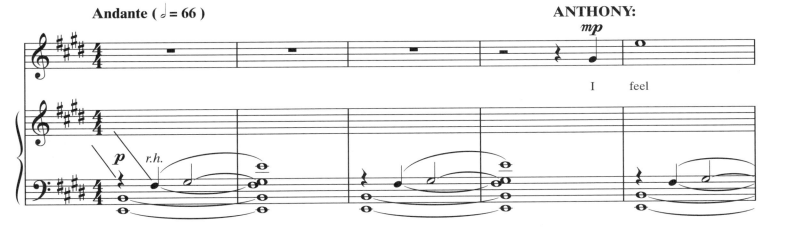

Johanna - 15 - 1
30013

dow.                    I am in the dark, be - side_____ you,

bur - ied sweet - ly in your    yel - low hair,    Jo - han - na..._____

**Allegretto** (♩ = 80)

TODD:

And   are   you   beau - ti - ful   and   pale,   With yel - low hair,_____   like   her?

I'd want you beau-ti-ful and pale, The way I've dreamed___ you were, Jo-

**ANTHONY:**

Jo - han - na..._____

han - na..._____

And if you're beau-ti-ful, what then, With yel-low hair_____ like wheat?

104

Johanna - 15 - 4
30013

106

Johanna - 15 - 6
30013

Mis-chief!  Mis-chief!

**TODD:**

And if I nev-er hear your voice, My tur-tle-dove,____ my dear,

I still have rea-son to re-joice: The way a-head____ is clear, Jo-

112

**TODD:** *mp*

And though I'll think of you, I guess, un-til the day_____ I die,

I think I miss you less and less as ev-'ry day_____ goes by, Jo-

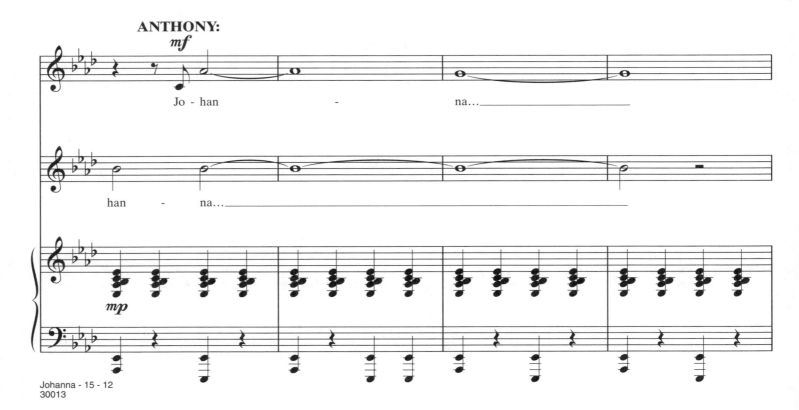

**ANTHONY:** *mf*

Jo - han - na..._____

han - na..._____

Johanna - 15 - 12
30013

# GOD, THAT'S GOOD!

Music and Lyrics by
STEPHEN SONDHEIM

**Moderato (♩ = 132)**

*(Instrumental cues)*

**L'istesso tempo**
**TOBIAS:**

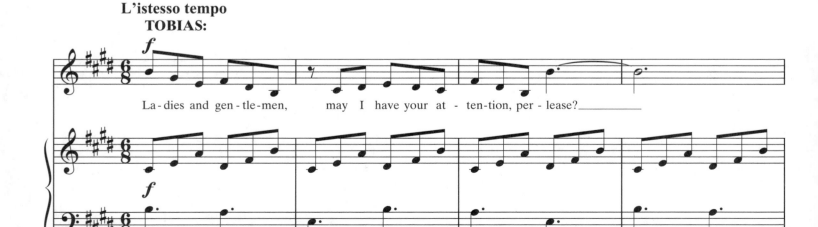

La - dies and gen - tle - men,  may I have your at - ten-tion, per - lease?

118

L'istesso tempo

God, That's Good! - 10 - 3
30013

**L'istesso tempo**
**MRS. LOVETT:**

Nice to see you, dear - ie. How have you been keep - ing?

Cor, me bones is wea - ry! To - by! One for the gen - tle - man...

Hear the bird - ies cheep - ing— Helps to keep it cheer - y...

To - by! *Throw the old wom - an out!*

God, That's Good! - 10 - 5
30013

$8^{vb}$

122

Eat them slow and feel the crust, how thin I rolled it. Eat them

**MRS. LOVETT:**

**TOBIAS:**

Eat them slow and feel the crust, how thin she rolled it. Eat them

God, That's Good! - 10 - 7
30013

slow, 'cause ev - 'ry-one's a prize. Eat them slow, 'cause

slow, 'cause ev - 'ry-one's a prize. Eat them slow, 'cause

that's the lot and now we've sold it! Come a - gain to - mor - row... Hold it!

that's the lot and now we've sold it! Come a - gain to - mor - row!

**MRS. LOVETT:**

Bless my eyes!

124

God, That's Good! - 10 - 9
30013

# BY THE SEA

Music and Lyrics by
STEPHEN SONDHEIM

**Moderato (♩ = 84)**

MRS. LOVETT: *(kisses him)* *(again)*

Ooh, Mis-ter Todd, I'm so hap-py I could

*(again)*

eat you up, I real-ly could. You know what I'd like to do, Mis-ter Todd?

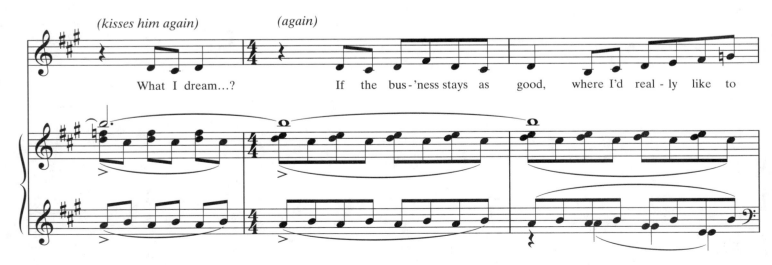

*(kisses him again)* *(again)*

What I dream...? If the bus-'ness stays as good, where I'd real-ly like to

By the Sea - 7 - 1
30013

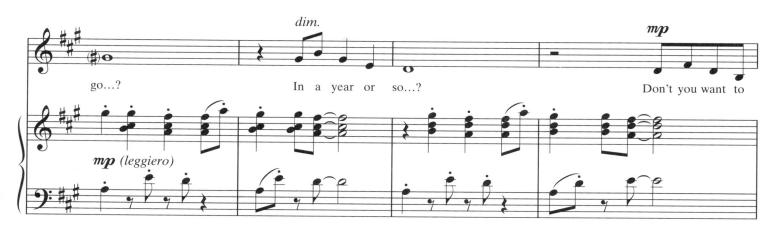

127

know you'd love__ it! You and me, Mis-ter T, we could be a - lone__ In a

house wot we'd al-most own.__ Down by the sea! Would-n't that be

**TODD:**

An - y-thing you say.__

smash - ing?_____ Think how snug it-'ll be un-der-

neath our flan - nel When it's just you and me and the En-glish Chan-nel. In our

130

rum - pled bed - ding le - git - i - mized. Me eye - lid - 'll flut - ter, I'll

turn in - to but - ter The mo - ment I mut - ter, "I do - hoo!"

132

By the Sea - 7 - 7
30013

# NOT WHILE I'M AROUND

Music and Lyrics by
STEPHEN SONDHEIM

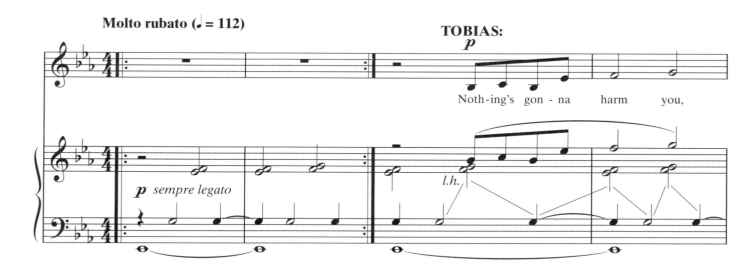

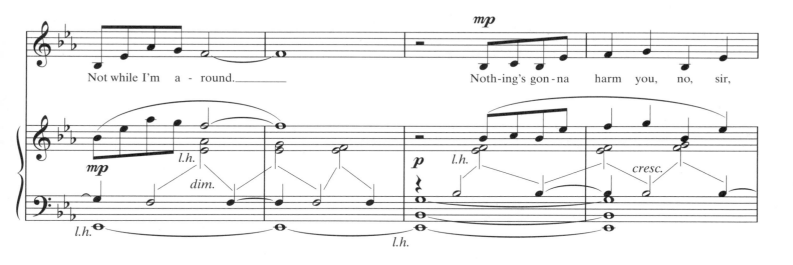

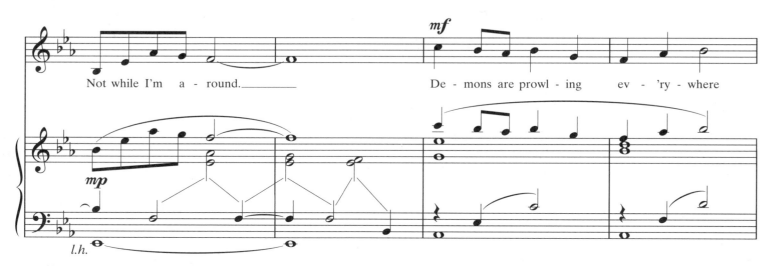

Not While I'm Around - 7 - 1
30013

134

Lyrics:
now-a-days._____ I'll send 'em howl-ing, I don't care...

I got ways._____

No one's gon-na hurt you, No one's gon-na dare._____

Oth-ers can de-sert you. Not to wor-ry, Whis-tle, I'll be there._____

**Tempo primo**

some.

(Under dialogue)

*mp* espressivo

**MRS. LOVETT:**
*Now Toby, dear, haven't we had enough foolish chatter?*
*Here, how about I give you a shiny new penny and you can go and get us some toffees?*

**TOBIAS:**
*That's Signor Pirelli's purse!*

**MRS. LOVETT:**
*No, it's not.*
*Just something Mr. T give me for my birthday.*

**TOBIAS:**
*That proves it.*
*We gotta go, ma'am – we gotta find the Beadle and get the law here –*

**MRS. LOVETT:**
*Shhh, Toby.*
*Hush, now, you're not going anywhere.*
*You just sit here nice and quiet, next to me.*
*That's right.*

**Più mosso espressivo**

*sempre* ***p***

*poco rit.*

*a tempo*

138

**Tempo primo**

*poco rit.*      *a tempo*      *poco rit.*

*a tempo*      *poco rit.*      *p*     *l.h.*

**MRS. LOVETT:**
*mp*

Noth-ing's gon - na harm you, Not while I'm A - round._____

*molto espressivo*
*r.h.*

*l.h.*

*l.h.*

Noth-ing's gon - na harm you, dar - ling, Not while I'm A - round._____

**TOBIAS:**

De - mons - 'll charm you with a smile For a while, But in time

Noth-ing's gon - na harm you, Not while I'm a - round.

Not While I'm Around - 7 - 7
30013